Illustrations: Ann de Bode
Original title: *Bang voor de bende*
© Van In, Lier, 1997. Van In Publishers, Grote Markt 39,
2500 Lier, Belgium.
© in this edition Evans Brothers Limited 1999
(world English rights excluding the USA and Canada)
English text by Su Swallow

First published in Great Britain by
Evans Brothers Limited
2A Portman Mansions
Chiltern Street
London W1M 1LE

Printed in Belgium by Hendrix

0 237 51 952 6

HELPING HANDS

PAY UP, OR ELSE!

ANN DE BODE AND RIEN BROERE

Evans Brothers Limited

Robert and Philip were on their way to school.
They often went to school together.
They had been good friends for a long time.
But now Robert was worried about his friend.
Philip had been very quiet lately,
and he never seemed to want to play any more.
'I don't feel like doing anything,' Philip would say.
Robert thought perhaps his friend was ill.

When they got to school, they saw... the Gang!
Three boys and two girls,
who were all older than Robert and Philip.
The whole school was afraid of them.
'Look who's here,' one of them called out.
'It's Philip!'
'Do you know the Gang?' Robert asked Philip in surprise.
'Sort of,' replied Philip.

Later, when the whole class were working hard,
the teacher suddenly clapped his hands.
'Listen, everyone,' he said.
'Something very worrying has happened.
Philip has lost his beautiful new pen.
He is the fourth person to lose something.
I think there must be a thief in our class.

Robert looked round at his classmates.
He couldn't believe that one of them was a thief.
But then, it wouldn't really show on their faces,
he thought. So it could be anyone.
He noticed Monica staring at him.
Perhaps she thinks that I'm the thief,
thought Robert, going red.

At playtime, they all got together.
'What a pity about your pen,' said Robert.
Philip hung his head. He looked very sad.
'It was a present from my grandad,' he said.
'It was silver, and very expensive.
My mum will be very cross.'
'But it was stolen. It wasn't your fault, was it?'
'No, you're right,' sighed Philip.

7

Robert looked as if he was thinking very hard
about his maths. But he wasn't - he was
thinking about the thief.
We must do something, he decided.
But what? He didn't know.
Could the police help?
Would they bother about just a pen?
The questions went round and round in his head.

8

Robert thought for a long time.
A thief at school. It just wasn't possible!
Somebody had to do something!
Suddenly, his face burst into a smile.
The smile of someone who had
just come up with a good idea!
Robert had a plan.
After school he would ask Philip to help him.

'I've got a plan,' said Robert.
'You and I are going to be detectives.
We will find the thief,
and people will read about us in the newspaper.'
'About you, perhaps, but not about me,' said Philip.
'I can't help you. I'm going home.'
 And Philip walked off.
 What kind of a friend is that? wondered Robert.

All right, then, thought Robert.
I'll do it by myself.
I am secret agent R, the brilliant detective.
Secret agent R is as sly as a fox,
brave as a lion, fast as a tiger, and eagle-eyed.
Look out! Secret agent R is on the case!

Robert reached a patch of wasteland.
He saw a group of children. It was the Gang.
And Philip, his best friend Philip, was with them!
Perhaps the Gang were pestering him?
This was something for secret agent R to investigate.
Robert ducked down behind a hedge
to spy on them without being seen.

Robert spied on the Gang.
Philip seemed very quiet.
The Gang seemed to be threatening him.
Then Philip took something out of his pocket
and gave it to one of the boys.
It looked shiny, but Robert couldn't see what it was.

Suddenly, Philip dashed off.
Robert dived down behind the hedge.
He could hear Philip panting, and
thought he might even be crying.
What ever is going on? wondered Robert.
He must talk to his friend very soon
and try to find out.

Oh dear! As Robert moved away from the hedge,
he came face to face with the Gang.
'Well, well,' said one of the girls.
'Look who's here. Philip's friend.
Have you brought us some stuff too?'
That's when Robert saw something shiny in her hand.
It was Philip's pen!

Robert forgot he was frightened. He just felt angry.
'Thieves!' he shouted. 'That pen isn't yours!'
'We didn't steal anything,' the girl replied.
'Your friend does th —'
'Shhh!' shouted one of the boys.
'You'll give the game away.
And as for you,' he said to Robert, 'Keep
your mouth shut, or we'll beat you up.'

16

Robert spent the rest of the day worrying
about the Gang. He couldn't even read his book.
Whatever did the Gang mean about Philip?
Then Robert remembered the girl with
Philip's pen in her hand. They must be the thieves!
He would have to talk to Philip about it.

The next day, when Robert met Philip,
he burst out, 'The thieves! Your pen!
The Gang!' The words fell over themselves
in his hurry to explain everything.
'The Gang stole your pen. I saw it myself.
We must tell the teacher everything.'

But Philip didn't look very happy.
His eyes opened wide with fright, and
he went bright red.
'N-no, no!' he stammered.
'Don't say anything to the teacher.
Please don't. Just forget it.'
Robert stared at his friend in astonishment.
He didn't understand what was going on.

A bit later, Robert came back from the toilets.
He heard the classroom door open.
Someone came out into the corridor.
Robert, secret agent R, pressed up against the wall
and held his breath. He waited,
then peered round the corner.
When he saw what was happening,
he felt cold all over.

Someone was searching the coat pockets!
It's the thief! thought Robert.
He looked again. That sweater...those
trousers...those shoes!
He recognised them! He knew who the thief was!
And he had never been more shocked in his life.

Soon, the thief disappeared.
Robert heard the classroom door open and close.
The thief was back in class.
Philip! thought Robert. It was Philip!
Robert stood very still. He didn't know what to do.
He had just found out who the thief was,
but it was his best friend.

Robert was very confused. He couldn't concentrate.
Should he say something? Or keep quiet?
When it was time to go home, Robert waited behind.
'What's up, Robert?' asked the teacher.
'Is something wrong?'
  Robert swallowed hard. His legs were shaking.
'I - I know who the thief is,' he muttered.

'Oh, so who is it then?' asked the teacher.
'Philip,' whispered Robert. 'Philip is the thief.'
And he told the teacher everything he had seen.
About how he saw Philip with the Gang, and
the girl with Philip's pen, and
his friend in the corridor...
'So that's it,' said the teacher, who
seemed to understand.

At first Robert felt relieved, then he felt like crying.
'Are you going to say it was me who told?' he asked.
'Don't worry, you were quite right to tell me,'
said the teacher. 'I even think you have helped Philip.
Leave it to me. I will explain later. First, I must make
quite sure who is to blame before I say anything.'

Now Robert was the secret agent with a big secret.
The next day, he said nothing.
Just before playtime, the headmistress came in.
She asked Philip to go with her.
Philip looked very worried.
Poor Philip, thought Robert.

At playtime, Philip still hadn't come back.
Robert couldn't stop thinking about him.
Then the headmistress came out,
with a face like thunder.
She walked over to the Gang and spoke to them.
They all looked scared.
She told them to go inside.

Later, when everyone was working,
Philip came back into the classroom.
He looked over at Robert, who
buried his head in his book.
But he noticed that Philip had been crying,
and now he looked angry. Had someone
told him it was Robert who had let on?

It was the end of the day.
The teacher sent everyone home.
'Robert, can you stay behind to help me?'
The room was empty, apart from Robert and the teacher.
'What do you want me to do?' asked Robert.
'Nothing,' said the teacher. 'I just needed an excuse for you to stay behind for a while.
I want to explain about the thefts.'

29

'It was the Gang who made Philip steal.
He had to steal and give them everything.
And if he hadn't they would have beaten him up.
Philip was afraid, so he did what they wanted.
But the Gang wanted more and more - even
his beautiful pen. That's why he
pretended it was stolen.'

'Nearly every day, they would wait for him.
Philip didn't dare tell anyone.
But now, their secret is out, and they
will be severely punished, believe me.'
'And Philip?' asked Robert, anxiously.
'Not Philip. He's suffered enough as it is.'
Thank goodness, thought Robert.
Philip had seemed to be a thief, but he wasn't really!

As he left the school, Robert saw Philip.
He didn't know what to say.
It was hard to act normally, after all that had happened.
But I have to do something, thought Robert.
And he walked slowly towards his friend.

'Hi!' said Robert after a while.
'Hi!' Philip answered.
They were both quiet.
'Hey, do you want to come over and
play later on?' asked Robert.
'Yes, thanks,' Philip replied.
Nothing more needed to be said.
Friends need few words to understand each other.

33